THE NATIONAL WEATHER SERVICE

SCIENTISTS AT WORK

THE NATIONAL

WEATHER SERVICE

Melvin Berger

The John Day Company • New York

The John Day Company, 257 Park Avenue South, New York, N.Y. 10010
an Intext publisher

Published on the same day in Canada by Longman Canada Limited.

Library of Congress Catalogue Card Number: 72-135276
Printed in the United States of America
Designed by The Etheredges

For Nancy

CONTENTS

ACKNOWLEDGMENTS 7

FOREWORD 9

WEATHERMEN AT YOUR SERVICE 13

THE WEATHER OBSERVER 18

THE UPPER-AIR SCIENTIST 35

THE RADAR OPERATOR 46

SENDING THE WEATHER REPORT 52

RECEIVING THE WEATHER MESSAGE 56

THE FORECASTER 70

AIR POLLUTION FORECASTER 75

THE CLIMATOLOGIST 82

THE HURRICANE HUNTERS 85

THE TORNADO FORECASTER 95

THE FLOOD FORECASTER 102

SPACEFLIGHT METEOROLOGISTS 107

CHANGING THE WEATHER 112

FURTHER READING 121

INDEX 123

ACKNOWLEDGMENTS

Many men of the National Weather Service contributed to the writing of this book:

Gerald Shak of the Eastern Region Office and Herbert Lieb and William West of the Office of Public Information were most kind in arranging visits to Weather Service offices, in making suggestions, and in furnishing needed material.

The staffs of the Albany, New York, Weather Service office, and of the John F. Kennedy International Airport, La Guardia Airport, and Rockefeller Center offices of the New York City Weather Service added to the book by sharing with me their excitement about being weather scientists, and by giving me permission to observe and photograph their daily activities.

I am particularly grateful to Ernest C. Johnson, Meteorologist in Charge, Albany Weather Service, for allowing me to make an extended visit to the Albany station. The book is largely based on the activities of the meteorologists in Albany. To give the reader a complete picture of Weather Service activities, though, descriptions of some special projects at other stations have been included.

FOREWORD

The old saying "Everybody talks about the weather but no-body does anything about it" is not quite true any more. After visiting with some of the Weather Service's offices Melvin Berger has written simply and clearly of many things the weathermen are doing about the weather.

The main purpose of *The National Weather Service* is to provide the reader with a comprehensive review of what it really means to be a "weatherman." Weathermen are a dedicated group of public servants. The challenge of being a weatherman is great but, even so, few leave the service for other careers. The author has demonstrated how complicated forecasting really is and makes it easier to understand why some forecasts are not correct.

In 1970 the United States Weather Service celebrated its century of progress, having first begun under the Signal Corps. In 1891 it was turned over to the Department of Agriculture, and later to the Department of Commerce. Progress in weather forecasting has been slow, but now it seems that meteorology is on the threshold of a true revolution. Recent advances in communications, the use of huge computers, and data received from satellites are ample evidence for future progress. Yet we must not expect perfection, for the complexity of the atmosphere is intimidating and the gaps in present knowledge are discouragingly large.

The National Weather Service takes you into the intimacy of the working offices which provide the many daily weather services used by the news media and the public at large. The Weather Service office at Albany, New York, is one such office. The author explains many of the routine "chores" that are essential at most of our offices. He has followed the forecasters and technicians, or weather observers, throughout their daily work, covering both surface observations and upper-air soundings. He takes the reader from the complex observing and public service office to the various centers that provide basic data and guidance to the many service offices. The Hurricane Hunters, tornado forecasters, spaceflight forecasters, the extensive National Meteorological Center, and the researchers are included.

Indeed, the reader should find this book interesting and informative for possible planning of a career, or just to understand what is behind the daily forecast.

> *Ernest C. Johnson*
> *Meteorologist in Charge*
> *Albany, New York, Weather Service*

THE NATIONAL WEATHER SERVICE

WEATHERMEN AT YOUR SERVICE

The telephone rings at the Weather Service station. A caller wants to get the latest weather report.

One of the weathermen on duty answers the phone. He reads the report: MOSTLY CLOUDY AND COOL TODAY, WITH THE RAIN ENDING THIS EVENING; HIGH IN THE UPPER 50's. FORECAST FOR TOMORROW, PARTLY SUNNY, WITH MODERATE TEMPERATURES.

The caller thanks the weatherman and hangs up. He is satisfied. He knows today's weather and what weather to expect for tomorrow. Now he can go ahead and make his plans.

Most people who call the Weather Service for weather reports,

The weatherman gives the weather report over the telephone. He gets his information from the maps and reports hanging over his desk.

or who read them in the paper, do not realize what goes into preparing this simple-sounding weather report.

There are more than three hundred Weather Service stations all over the United States. About ten to twenty weathermen work at an average station. Most of them went to college or to special schools to learn how to be weathermen. They were taught the science of weather, or meteorology. They are meteorologists and meteorological technicians.

At each Weather Service station the meteorological technicians use many different instruments to observe and measure the weather. They prepare reports that describe the weather conditions at the station.

The meteorologists at the Weather Service stations forecast, or predict, what the weather will be over the next hours or days. The forecaster uses the weather observations of his fellow technicians at the station. He also receives information from other stations, airplanes, weather satellites, and computers. All of these resources provide him with a basis for his forecast of the weather.

In addition to the general forecasts that serve all the people, there are special weather services. Airplane pilots come to the Service to ask about the weather along their routes. They change their flight plans if the weatherman warns of bad weather. Farmers depend on detailed weather information to decide on their planting and harvesting schedules. Ship captains go miles out of their way to avoid a storm that is forecast by the Weather Service. Spacemen depend on weather information to help plan the time for a space shot and the place for the splashdown.

The meteorologists at the Weather Service also issue early storm warnings. Many lives have been saved by forecasts of approaching blizzards, hurricanes, tornadoes, or severe thunder and lightning storms. They keep a close watch on air pollution in the big cities. They warn of the danger of forest fires and floods. They have complete weather records to give information on the climate in each city and throughout the rural areas. And now they are doing research on ways to change the weather.

There are meteorologists on duty at the Weather Service stations day and night, every single day of the year. They watch the changing weather, they issue forecasts and storm warnings, and they offer many special services. All of their work has one goal—to serve you.

Although the Weather Service gave an early warning of the approaching snowstorm, these Chicago cars and buses tried to get through.

ESSA

17

THE WEATHER OBSERVER

The weather observer is one of the busiest technicians at the Weather Service. He is in charge of observing, measuring, and describing weather conditions at the station.

The observer may have a long drive to his job. The station is located at the airport, just outside the city. He parks his car in front of a small building, not far from the main passenger terminal. He walks in, past a sign that reads U.S. DEPARTMENT OF COMMERCE, WEATHER SERVICE.

He arrives a few minutes before 8 o'clock in the morning. He will be on duty until 4 o'clock that afternoon. Since the Weather Service is open twenty-four hours a day, there are three shifts—8 to 4, 4 to midnight, and midnight to 8 A.M. The observer works a different shift each week. Some men do not mind changing their schedules. Others cannot get used to the idea and leave the Weather Service for that reason.

The day observer speaks to the man who has been on duty during the night. Together they go over the developing weather patterns. The night observer points out the features that he thinks should be watched.

At 8 o'clock it is time for the observer to make his first observations. He pulls a large pad of paper toward him. This is the Daily Record. It is lined and divided into many separate columns. Every hour he will enter his weather observations here. By the end of the day all of the blank spaces will be filled in.

The date, the hour, and his initials go on first. The next few columns call for a description of the sky—the type, amount, height, and movement of the clouds.

The Weather Service Office has many large windows. Most of the sky can be seen from indoors. The observer could easily guess at what clouds are beyond his immediate view. But he realizes that the work of the Weather Service depends on true, accurate observations, not on guesses. So, no matter how bad the weather, the observer goes up to the roof every hour to make his cloud observations.

His eyes scan the horizon. On the Daily Record he jots down the percentage of the sky that is covered by clouds. He uses a code sign to show the type of clouds. And he makes an estimate of the cloud height and the direction and speed that they are moving.

The observer has two tools that he uses for more exact measure-

Station __NEW YORK, N. Y.__   CENTRAL PARK   Date __SATURDAY, MAY 23, 1970__

Time (EST) (1)	Temperature (°F) (2)	Precipitation (inches) (3)	WIND Direction (4)	WIND Speed (m.p.h.) (5)	Sunshine (minutes) (6)	Atmospheric Solar Radiation (Langleys) (7)	Weather (8)	FAST WIND When over 29 mph Direction & speed (mph) (10)	Time (EST) (11)	PEAK GUST 20 MPH OR MORE (12)	Relative Humidity % (13)	Dew point (13a)	Beginnings and endings of meteorological phenomena Remarks, Notes, etc. (14)	Sea Level Pressure inches (14a)	Time (EST) (1)
0059	71		SW	6							85	66		29.92	0059
0159	70		SW	5							87	66		29.92	0159
0259	68		W	4							87	64		29.93	0259
0359	68		NW	5							81	62		29.95	0359
0459	67		NW	5	0	0.3					81	61	SUNRISE 0432	29.96	0459
0559	67		W	7	6	4.2					81	61		29.96	0559
0659	69		NW	5	13	15.8					76	61	MOONSET 0615	29.98	0659
0759	69		NW	3	1	9.6					76	61		29.98	0759
0859	72		N	4	1	29.0					73	63		29.97	0859
0959	74		N	6	26	46.2					66	63		29.99	0959
1059	74		NE	6	1	36.4					66	63		30.00	1059
1159	74		N	6	0	21.7					66	62		29.99	1159
1259	77		NE	6	3	51.7					62	63		29.99	1259
1359	71		E	10	0	34.4					68	60		29.99	1359
1459	71		E	8	0	32.5					68	60		29.98	1459
1559	71		E	10	0	29.5					68	60		29.96	1559
1659	65	.02	E	9	0	4.0	R				84	60	Rb 1610 - Re 1720	29.98	1659
1759	62	T	E	7	0	2.9					90	59		30.00	1759
1859	61		E	7	0	1.4					87	57		30.01	1859
1959	60	.02	SE	6	0	0.0	R				86	56	SUNSET 1913 Rb 1913 Re 2015	30.02	1959
2059	60	T	E	4							90	57		30.02	2059
2159	60		NE	7							90	57		30.02	2159
2259	59		E	7							93	57	MOONRISE 2229	30.03	2259
2359	59		NE	5							93	57		30.03	2359
SUM	—	.04		148	45	319.6	—								
AVER	—	—	Prevailing 6.2				—								
MISC	—	—	E		Poss. 881	5 %	—								

SYMBOLS USED IN COLUMNS 9 AND 14

A — HAIL	R — RAIN	DL — DISTANT LIGHTNING
E — SLEET	S — SNOW	ZL — FREEZING DRIZZLE
L — DRIZZLE	T — THUNDERSTORM	ZR — FREEZING RAIN

SCHEDULED OBSERVATIONS

Time (EST) (15)	Sea Level Pressure inches (16)	Dry Bulb (17)	Wet Bulb (18)	Dew point (19)	Rel. Hu- mid. (20)	Temperature Max (21)	Temperature Min (22)	Precipitation (23)	Snowfall (24)	Snow Depth (25)	(26)
0050	29.92	70.9	67.6	66.0	85	79	68	.39	0	0	
0650	29.98	69.0	63.9	61.0	76	71	67	0	0	0	
1250	29.99	77.1	67.8	63.0	62	78	69	0	0	0	
1850	30.01	60.7	58.5	57.0	87	77	61	.02	0	0	

SUMMARY OF DAY (Midnight to Midnight)

Temperature 24-Hour Max (27)	Temperature 24-Hour Min (28)	Average Temperature (29)	Normal Temperature (30)	24 Hour Precip (Water Equiv.) (31)	24 Hour Snowfall Unmltd (32)	Snow Depth As of 6:50AM (33)	Wind (M.P.H.) Fastest Mile and Direction (34)	Time (LST) (35)	Heating Degree Days (36)
78 1235	59 2230	69	65	.04	0	0	13E	1325	0

ESSA

After the Daily Record is filled out by hand, a typewritten copy is prepared.

ments. The simplest one is a small balloon, called a ceiling balloon. The ceiling balloon is filled with an exact amount of helium gas, so that it will rise at a fixed speed. The observer releases the balloon and follows its flight. He measures the time it takes for the balloon to disappear into the clouds. Then he can calculate the distance to the bottom of the cloud.

Another device for measuring cloud height is the ceilometer. One part of the ceilometer projects a powerful rotating light beam up at the clouds. Four hundred feet away a detector picks up the reflected light. The ceilometer automatically calculates the height of the clouds.

While he is on the roof, the observer also checks the visibility. He looks for several landmarks around the station—the water tower at the airport, a church steeple in a nearby town, some distant mountain peaks. He knows the distance to each of these points. The farthest one he can see gives him a measure of visibility.

When the observer sees these clouds he knows that a thunderstorm is on its way.

ESSA

*The ceilometer projecting
its powerful rotating light beam
up at the clouds.*

ESSA

*The ceilometer detector
picks up the reflected light,
as a plane comes in
for a landing at the airport.*

M. Berger

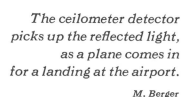

In bad weather it is important to know the exact visibility at the airport. The tool that gives him this figure is the transmissometer.

The transmissometer consists of two low towers, about five hundred feet apart. They are usually set alongside one of the airport's runways. A light in one tower shines directly on a window in the other. By measuring the brightness of the received light, the transmissometer automatically measures the visibility.

Not long ago, the transmissometer at a Weather Service station showed lower and lower visibility each day. Finally, the observer went out to investigate. He soon found the problem. A family of birds was building a nest in the tube through which

An identical tower,
500 feet away,
receives the light
from the transmissometer to
measure visibility.

the light beam passed. He carefully removed the nest—and the transmissometer, once again, gave correct visibility readings.

As soon as the observer has checked the clouds and visibility, he heads back to the station. He seats himself in front of a large metal cabinet containing several different dials. There are also pens drawing ink lines on long rolls of graph paper.

This is the observation panel. Each of the dials and pens is measuring or recording some aspect of the weather. A glance at the panel gives the observer all the details of weather at the station.

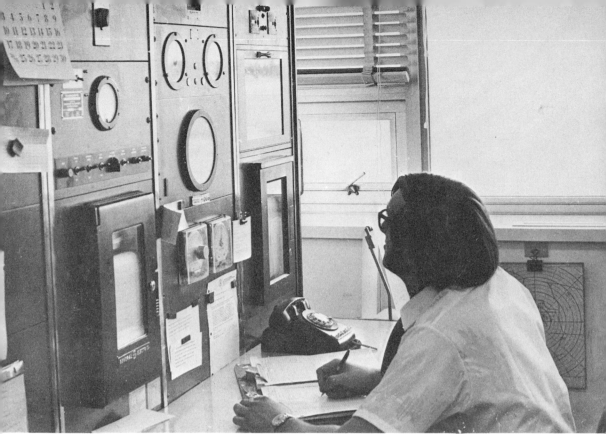

M. Berger

The observer reads the dials on the observation panel to fill in the Daily Record.

Sixty-three degrees on the thermometer dial—a nice, spring day.

M. Berger

Most of the instruments that actually measure the weather are located out in the middle of the airport, far from the building. These modern weather instruments work by electricity. The measurements they make are carried by wires to the observation panel, where they are read by the observer.

The observer places the Daily Record on the narrow ledge in front of the observation panel. He is ready now to fill in more of the items on the first of his hourly observations.

First, the temperature. An outdoor mechanical thermometer is used. The rise or fall of the air temperature bends a metal element. As it moves, a changing electrical signal is sent to the pointer on the observation panel. The observer jots down the temperature shown by the pointer.

The next column calls for the precipitation measurement—how much rain, snow, hail, or sleet has fallen in the last hour. Precipitation is measured by a precipitation gage which is either on the roof or somewhere on the ground near the station.

The common precipitation gage looks like a big can, with an opening on top. The precipitation falls into a pail inside the can. The pail rests on a scale. When there is precipitation, it increases the weight of the pail. The increase in weight is translated into inches of rain on the observation panel. The observer notes the amount of precipitation and enters it on the Daily Record.

Two wind measurements are called for next—direction and speed. The direction is measured by a weather vane. The vane is usually a flat piece of metal that is shaped to a point at one end. It is attached on top of a pole so that it is free to turn in all directions. As the wind blows, the vane turns to face the direction from which the wind is blowing. If the wind is blowing from the west,

The observer checks the rain gage on the roof.

The dials showing wind speed and direction on the observation panel.

the point of the vane faces west. This wind is then called a west wind.

The weather vane is also connected by electricity to a pointer on the observation panel. As the vane turns, the pointer indicates the wind direction—north, south, east, or west—on a dial.

On the same pole as the weather vane is another instrument with three round cups extending out to the sides. This instrument is called an anemometer. It measures the speed of the wind.

The wind catches the cups of the anemometer. It makes them spin around. The stronger the wind, the faster the anemometer cups whirl. As the anemometer turns, electrical contacts measure the speed. The speed shows up as miles per hour on the observation panel.

The weatherman goes out
to the wind vane and anemometer
to make sure that
they are working properly.

ESSA

29

Temperature and precipitation readings change slowly. But changes in wind direction and speed come very quickly. The pointers on the panel swing back and forth. The observer watches both dials for about one minute. He estimates the average direction and average speed. These are the figures he then places in the Daily Record.

Humidity, or moisture, is the amount of water vapor in the air. One of the instruments used to measure humidity is the hair hygrometer. It is based on the fact that human hairs get slightly longer when they are wet.

In the hair hygrometer several hairs, usually blond, are stretched over a metal frame. A pointer attached to one end of the frame moves as the hair length changes. The amount of change is an accurate measure of the percentage of humidity in the air.

Sometimes a hygrometer and thermometer are joined in a single instrument called a hygrothermometer. It measures both humidity and temperature. The hygrothermometer can be arranged to draw a continuous ink line of its measurements. It is then called a hygrothermograph.

The next panel window that the observer checks gives him a reading on the air pressure. The air pressure is measured by a barometer.

The aneroid barometer is the most frequently used type at the Weather Service. It consists of a small sealed box made of thin, flexible metal. The air is removed from inside the box, and a stiff spring keeps it from collapsing. A metal pointer is attached to one end of the box.

When the outside air pressure is high, the box is squeezed smaller, and the pointer moves in one direction. When the air

Human hairs, usually blond,
are used in the
hygrometer to measure humidity.

ESSA

A hygrometer and thermometer are sometimes combined in a single instrument that measures both humidity and temperature.

pressure is low, the box grows larger, and the pointer moves in the opposite direction.

The barometer is the only tool that is kept inside the observation panel. There is no need to keep the barometer outside with the other instruments. The air pressure is the same, indoors or out.

The weatherman points to the dial of the hygrothermometer. The instrument itself is in the large can to the right.

The metal pointer of the aneroid barometer is sometimes set up to draw a line on graph paper, making a permanent record of the changing air pressure. The barometer is then called a barograph.

The last space on the top line of the Daily Record is for general comments on the weather. The observer notes the times of sunrise and sunset, whether there is any rain or snow, thunder or

ESSA

The barograph (left) keeps a record of the air pressure. The barometer (right) shows it on a dial. Both are usually kept in the observation panel.

lightning, and any other outstanding features of the weather.

The hourly weather report is now complete. The observer checks his figures. He knows how important they are. An entire crop of oranges or lemons can be lost because the temperature report was a few degrees too high, and the farmer did nothing to prevent frost. A city can be paralyzed by stuck cars if the snow-fall forecast report is too low, and everyone thinks it is safe to drive. A plane can crash because of a mistake in the wind speed report.

In between his hourly reports the observer leaves the observation panel. He answers some of the telephone calls that are always coming into the station. And he works with other weather technicians in the different activities of the Weather Service.

Now he joins with the upper-air weatherman to collect weather information about the atmosphere miles above the station.

THE UPPER-AIR SPECIALIST

"Weather balloon being released."

Twice a day this message flashes from the Weather Service station to the airport control tower. All planes in the area are warned to be on the alert for the large weather balloon being launched. At 7:15 A.M. and 7:15 P.M. upper-air scientists at nearly one hundred Weather Service stations send up weather balloons. The balloons measure the weather conditions high in the upper air.

The upper-air specialist begins his preparations about one hour before launch time. From a metal cabinet he removes a

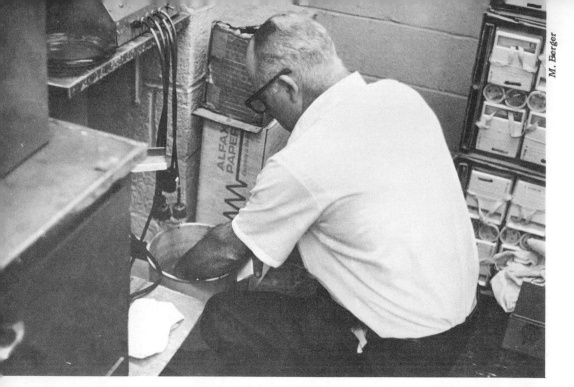

After removing the radiosonde from the closet behnd him, the upper-air scientist soaks the battery in water to start the flow of electricity.

white cardboard and plastic box. This is the instrument package, called a radiosonde, that will be attached to the balloon.

There are three tiny weather-measuring instruments in the radiosonde. An aneroid barometer measures the air pressure. A thermometer measures the temperature. And a hygrometer measures the humidity. There is also a small radio transmitter that is powered by a battery. The transmitter sends back the various measurements as the radiosonde rises through the air.

The specialist first takes the battery from the radiosonde and soaks it in water. Once it is wet, the battery starts to produce electricity. When he connects the battery into the radiosonde the

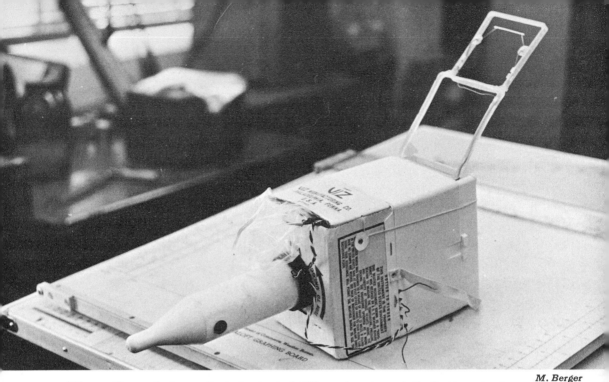

The radiosonde is ready to be tested. The extension at the bottom is the radio transmitter. The thin wire across the top is an electrical thermometer.

The radiosonde is tested in a weather box, where the exact weather conditions are known.

radio transmitter and the measuring instruments begin to work.

Next he switches on a large radio receiver. A high-pitched sound fills the room. The receiver is picking up the signal from the radiosonde.

To test the radiosonde, he places it in a special weather box. The exact weather conditions inside the box are known. The scientist then returns to the receiver and adjusts the instrument.

Once he is satisfied that everything is working properly, the

The upper-air scientist adjusts the radio receiver while testing the radiosonde.

M. Berger

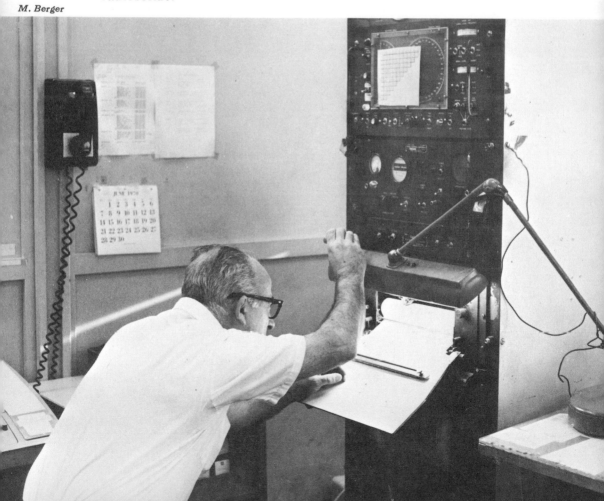

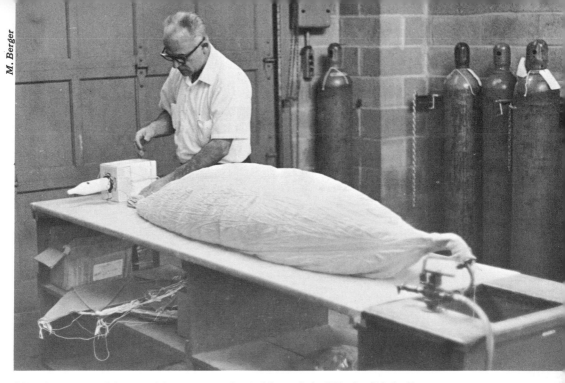

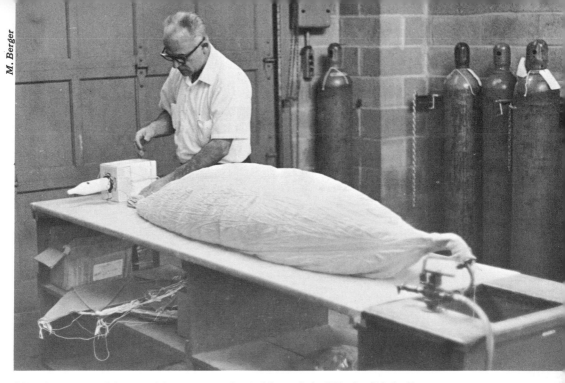

The balloon slides and jumps on the table as it is filled with helium gas.

upper-air specialist removes the radiosonde from the weather box. Holding it very securely, he leaves the main building. As he goes, he calls out to the observer to be ready to help him in a few minutes.

The weatherman enters a nearby building. It is small—no larger than a two-car garage—but much taller. This is the balloon inflation building.

Along one wall are large metal tanks of helium gas. Helium is lighter than air. When a balloon is inflated with helium, it will be carried aloft.

From a small warming oven, the scientist removes a light, tan-colored plastic balloon. The balloon is warmed to keep the plastic

39

flexible. He brings the balloon to a large wooden table in the center of the room and slips the neck of the balloon over a pipe that is connected to a helium tank. Then he turns on the gas.

As the gas hisses into the balloon it seems to come to life. It slides and jumps on the table as its folds and creases straighten out. After a few minutes, it begins to rise off the table very slowly.

The balloon grows bigger and bigger. Soon it is flying freely, held down only by the helium spout. When the balloon reaches full size, the flow of gas is cut off automatically.

With a length of string the specialist ties off the neck of the balloon. He then attaches a small, brightly colored paper parachute beneath the balloon. He ties the radiosonde to the parachute.

Everything is ready now for launch. The specialist speaks on a radio connection to the Weather Service office. He asks the observer, still back at the office, to check the radio antenna that will track the flight of the balloon.

The specialist also asks for a report on the surface winds. He must decide in advance the direction in which he will run as he launches the balloon. If he heads the wrong way, the delicate instrument package may be smashed against a building or dragged along the ground.

As soon as he is ready, he presses a button that opens the wall-sized door. With the clumsy eight-foot-tall balloon in one hand and the radiosonde in the other, he carefully heads out of the building.

Immediately the wind sends the balloon flailing wildly about. The specialist holds on tightly as he starts to run. Then he stops, spins around, and flings it up into the air. Quickly, gracefully, the balloon soars. The parachute and radiosonde swing gently underneath.

The weatherman gets the paper parachute ready to be tied to the balloon.

Holding on tightly to the big, clumsy balloon, the scientist starts his run. On the roof of the building behind him is the plastic dome containing the radio antenna.

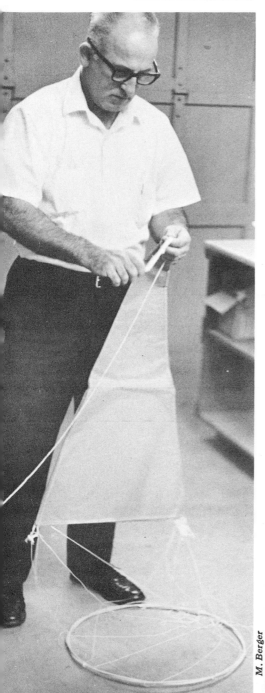

M. Berger

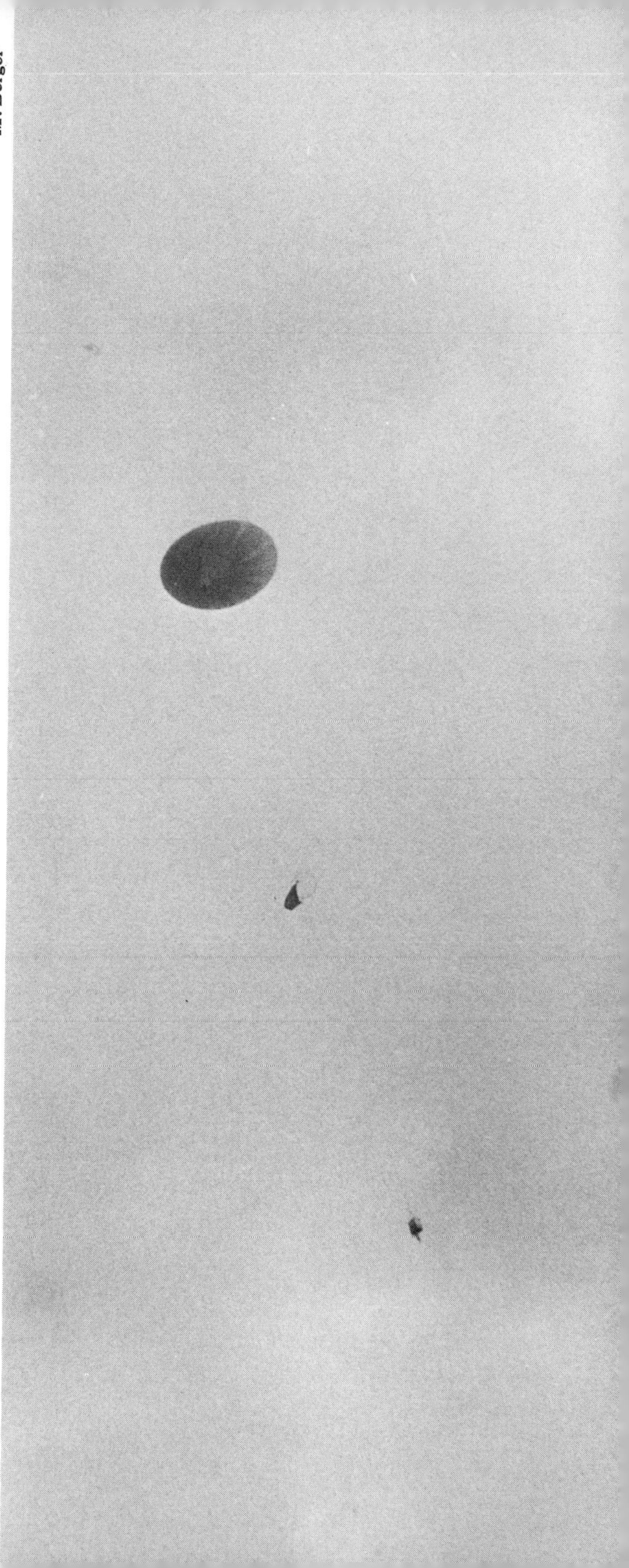

At the last minute
the upper-air scientist
spins around and
tosses the balloon up
into the air.

Quickly and gracefully the
balloon flies off,
with the parachute and
radiosonde dangling below.

The two weathermen talk again by radio. The man on the ground gives his estimate of the direction of the balloon's flight. The observer in the station confirms that the antenna is tracking and that the radio signal is being picked up. From then on the balloon will be followed automatically.

The upper-air specialist returns to the empty inflation building. He puts another balloon into the warming oven to be ready for the next launch. He closes the big door and heads back to the station.

For the next hour and a half the balloon continues to rise. It sends back a steady radio signal. This signal carries the measurements of pressure, temperature, and humidity at the upper-air levels through which the radiosonde is passing.

The signal moves a pen that is placed at the top of a long strip of graph paper. The paper is slowly moving out of the front of the radio receiver. The pen draws a line showing the changes in the measurements being radioed down from the radiosonde.

At the same time, another electronic device is making a record of the changing angle and direction of the tracking radio antenna. The upper-air specialist will later use this information to calculate the wind speed and direction at various heights above the surface.

As it rises, the balloon flies through thinner and thinner air. The outside air pressure keeps dropping, making the balloon grow larger. Finally, at a height of about twenty miles, the balloon bursts. The parachute opens, and the radiosonde floats slowly down to earth.

Of all the balloons that are launched each year, about 25 percent are found, usually 200 miles or so from where they were

Slowly the paper moves out of the radio receiver, with a permanent record of the weather measurements in the upper air.

launched. The finder is requested to return the radiosonde to the Weather Service. A good percentage of these are repaired and used again.

During the flight and after the balloon has burst, the upper-air specialist has the difficult task of organizing and plotting the data that has been radioed back. He prepares charts presenting the information in the standard form that all weathermen understand and use. He works out the wind patterns from the radio antenna data. This requires great care and patience as well as careful computations.

As soon as his charts are ready, the specialist brings them in to the main room of the station. They are placed alongside the Daily Record—another report on weather observations at this station.

THE RADAR OPERATOR

The radar operator works by himself in a dimly lit room. He sits in front of a large piece of electronic equipment. At the center is a round screen, similar to the screen of a television set.

This is the radar screen. Seated here the radar operator can spot rain, hail, and snow falling up to 250 miles away from the station.

The operator sees a thin beam of light slowly sweep around the screen. As it goes, it leaves some areas or spots white, while the rest of the screen remains dark. The bright places indicate that there is precipitation in the area.

On the roof of the Weather Service is a round, white plastic dome, about eighteen feet tall. Inside is the rotating radar antenna. The dome protects the antenna without interfering with its operation.

The radar antenna sends out invisible radio waves. When these waves strike raindrops, or snowflakes, the radio waves are reflected back. The same antenna receives the reflected waves and shows them as a pattern on the radar screen.

Circles marked on the radar screen show the distances from the antenna. A scale around the edge shows the points of the compass. By studying the screen the operator can tell the location of the precipitation and the direction that it is moving.

During periods of clear weather, the radar meteorologist just checks the radar every hour. But, during stormy weather, he is at the screen continuously. He keeps a written record of all his observations on the radar screen. Sometimes he marks the position of a disturbance on the screen with a special pencil. Then he can tell at a glance if it has moved.

There is also an automatic movie camera that takes a picture of the radar screen every few minutes. These photos help in the analysis of weather patterns. Occasionally, they help in determining the cause of an airplane accident.

Next to the main radar screen is a smaller one. This screen is marked to show height in miles. When the operator switches to this screen he can measure the height of the precipitation and see whether it is reaching the ground.

Using radar would be very simple if every storm showed up clearly on the screen, and no other images interfered. Unfortunately, it is not nearly that easy. Tall buildings, airplanes, and various electrical disturbances "dirty" up the radar picture. Also,

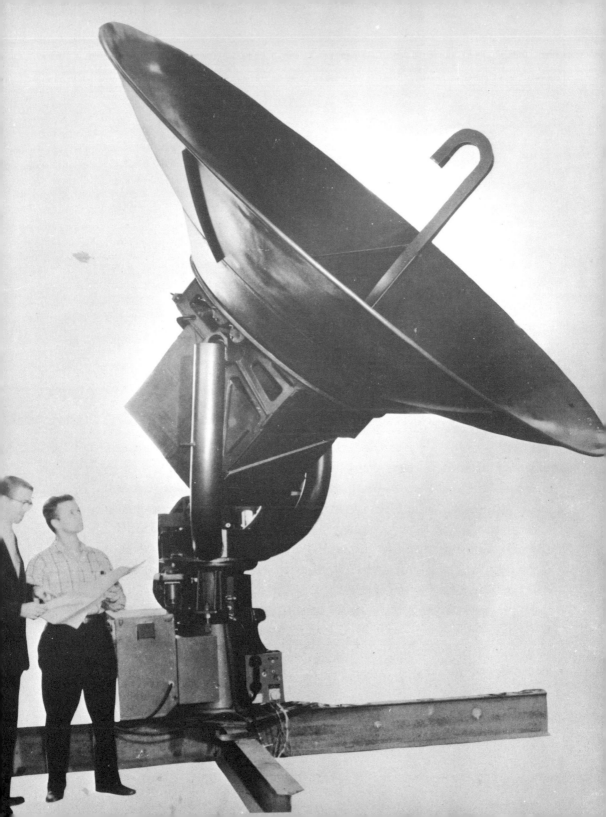

How radar works.

various weather systems show up differently on the radar screen.

The radar operator has special training beyond his studies in meteorology. He has learned to separate pictures of weather disturbances from other interference. And he is able to recognize and identify the type of weather disturbance from the picture that he sees on the radar screen.

Very often the radar operator is the first to spot the approach of bad weather. This advance information helps the Weather Service to warn communities of approaching storms.

Some years ago the radar operator at a local Weather Service station noticed a hailstorm developing to the west of the station. He noticed that it was growing in size. He also saw that it was moving rather quickly to the east.

A modern radar antenna.
It has a range of 250 miles.

*The radar operator
outlines the bad weather
he sees on the screen.*

ESSA

He realized that the center of the storm was heading directly toward a popular resort lake. There were many vacationers out in canoes and small boats on the lake.

The operator put through an emergency call to the State Police. Within minutes, the police and park rangers were out in motorboats on the lake, warning boaters to head for shelter.

Very soon after the warning went out, the hailstorm struck the lake. Along with the large hailstones, there were strong, gusty winds. But no one was hurt. At least three groups of boaters were saved by the alert radar operator and the quick action by the police.

Throughout the day, the radar operator adds his reports to those collected by the observer and the upper-air specialist. Taken

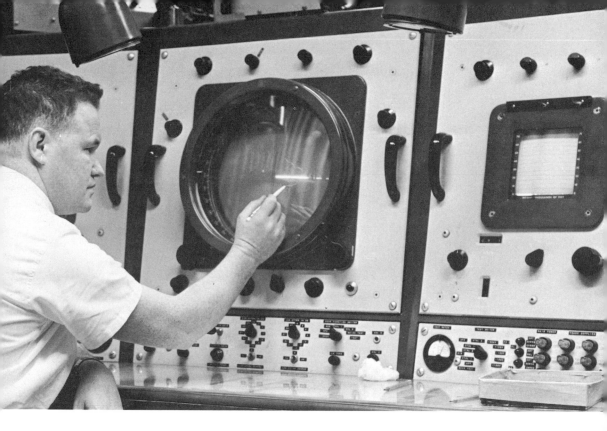

together they describe the weather at, above, and around the station. The forecaster uses these reports as the basis of his local weather forecast.

But, just as all the weathermen at the station work together as a team, so all the Weather Service stations cooperate to provide the very best weather service to the nation. An advanced electronic communication system links all of the offices together. Reports are sent back and forth between stations. Central offices collect various reports and send out summaries.

Each office has a communication room for sending and receiving weather messages. The communication room is a little-known, but most important part of every Weather Service station.

SENDING THE WEATHER REPORT

As each weatherman finishes his report, he rushes into the communication room. He is in a hurry to send it out on the teletype. Since the weather is always changing, it is important that the report go out just as soon as it is ready.

The teletypes, about eight machines that look like big, complicated typewriters, are along the walls of the communication room. They are connected to identical teletypes that may be located hundreds or thousands of miles away. When a message is typed on one teletype, it immediately appears on all the other teletypes.

In some ways, the teletype is similar to the telephone. You

talk into the telephone and your voice is immediately heard on another phone that is connected by wires to your phone. When the weatherman types a message on the teletype, it appears on the teletypes that are connected by wire to the sending teletype.

Each of the teletypes in the communication room is connected into a different circuit. There are local, regional, and national circuits. There are aviation and marine circuits. There is a storm-warning circuit. And there are teletypes that are connected to the police, the highway department, the newspapers, and the radio and television stations.

The weatherman sits down at one of the teletypes and types out his report. He does not send every word and number that appears in his report, though. If he included everything, it would clog up the lines, and all communication would be slowed down.

Instead, he reduces his report to a code. This keeps the message very short. In fact, one line of numbers includes an entire weather report. All weathermen know the code. They easily put the report into code, and can quickly interpret any report they see.

Here, as an example, is the coded copy of part of an actual weather report:

405 83220 12716 24731

These numbers may not tell you very much. But they give a trained weatherman an amazing amount of information.

405	The report is from the Washington, D.C., Weather Service.
8	Sky completely overcast
32	Wind from 320°, or northwest
20	Wind speed 20 knots
12	Visibility 12/16 (¾) of a mile

71 Light snow is falling
6 It has been raining
247 Air pressure 1024.7 millibars
31 Temperature 31°

The numbers in the rest of the report would describe the clouds, the precipitation, the humidity, and changes in the air pressure.

As the weatherman types out the coded message it appears on many other teletypes. Weathermen in other weather stations collect these messages to learn the weather details in different areas. Airlines use it to advise their pilots of the weather conditions. Radio and television stations use it to announce the weather on their news programs.

Many of the teletype messages also go to the hub of the entire teletype network, which is located in Suitland, Maryland, just outside Washington, D.C. It is the largest U.S. Weather Service office and is called the National Meteorological Center (NMC). Weather reports from all over the country and much of the world come pouring into the NMC on some forty separate teletype lines.

The meteorologists at the NMC use this data to prepare nationwide forecasts and weather maps. These are then sent back to individual Weather Service offices on the same teletype lines. And they are received on the teletypes in the communication room of each Weather Service office.

*As the weatherman types out
his report on the teletype, it
immediately appears on
other teletypes many miles away.*
ESSA

RECEIVING THE WEATHER MESSAGE

The communication room is the noisiest place in the entire Weather Service station. The teletypes clatter away with a terrible din as they bring in a never-ending stream of weather messages.

The messages appear on a wide strip of yellow paper that slowly moves up through each teletype. It is the job of each of the weathermen to spend some time in the communication room collecting these messages.

As each message is finished, the weatherman tears it off. He hangs many of them from hooks or clipboards on the wall. Some

The teletype messages are filed in the proper places.

he slips into folders. A few, of little interest to the local weather-men, he throws away.

Many of the messages received on the station's teletypes are from the NMC (National Meteorological Center). Every day the NMC collects thousands of weather reports. They come from

A ceremony marks the completion of a new antenna to receive messages from the weather satellites.

observers at Weather Service stations, from ships and planes, and from foreign weather bureaus.

In recent years a new source of weather data has been providing the NMC with much valuable information. On April 1, 1960, a giant rocket blasted off from Cape Kennedy, placing TIROS, the first weather satellite, into orbit around the earth.

A weather satellite being prepared for launch.

ESSA

Since then, many new and improved weather satellites have been launched. Several weather satellites are presently circling the earth and watching the global weather.

The weather satellites take photos of cloud patterns that cover the earth. They also measure the temperature on earth and at various heights above the earth. Satellite pictures very often give the first warning of developing hurricanes and other severe storms. They also show that clouds are organized into large-scale patterns and are not just scattered about.

COMPLETE VIEW OF NORTHERN HEMISPHERE

FEBRUARY 13, 1965   TIROS IX

1200 GMT   SURFACE ANALYSIS

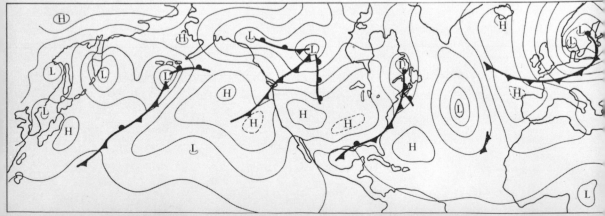

The photos and measurements from the satellites are radioed down to earth. They are received on sensitive radio antennas. The information joins the flow of data into the NMC.

As the reports arrive at the NMC they are fed into computers. The computers identify and sort the reports. They also check the figures. Any numbers that do not fit in with the others are rejected. The computers quickly produce an error-free summary of the weather reports that are received. These summaries are sent out on the teletypes from the NMC.

ATHER

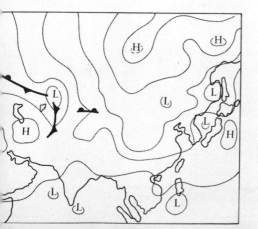

The first complete view of Northern Hemisphere weather. Notice the outline of the continents.

ESSA

The weather scientists carefully study the satellite cloud photos.

Meteorologists at the NMC also use these summaries to prepare weather maps that show weather conditions all over the
country. They use a code to translate these observations into
weather maps.

Here, as an example, is a coded station report as it appears on
a weather map prepared by the NMC. It contains the same infor-

mation as the coded teletype report sent out by the observer that was shown in the last chapter.

The summaries also go into a giant $15 million computer— one of the largest in the world. This computer does an analysis of the weather reports. It points out the outstanding features of the weather and shows general weather patterns across the country.

Attached to the computer is an electronic device — an automatic data plotter. A blank weather map is inserted. A metal arm with a pen attached to it moves over the map. Lines are drawn which show the results of the computer analysis.

At the same time, meteorologists at the NMC do their own analysis of the weather reports. They, too, prepare a weather map—by hand.

Their analysis is then compared with the computer analysis. The meteorologists discuss the differences. The best part of the human analysis is combined with the best part of the machine analysis. The result is returned to the computer.

An amazing thing then occurs. The weather analysis is advanced into the future. For each point on the map the computer calculates how the weather will be changing over the next ten minutes.

The computer keeps pushing into the future—ten minutes, after ten minutes, after ten minutes. Soon the computer has forecasts of what the weather will be in twelve, twenty-four, thirty-six, and finally forty-eight hours.

The entire computer operation takes a little more than one hour. In that time it performs more than 5 million separate steps. It is estimated that it would take 64,000 trained meteorologists, working day and night, to keep up with the computer.

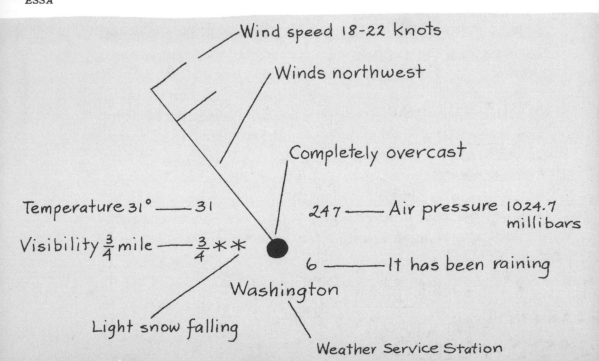

Wind speed 18-22 knots

Winds northwest

Completely overcast

Temperature 31° —— 31

247 —— Air pressure 1024.7 millibars

Visibility $\frac{3}{4}$ mile —— $\frac{3}{4}$ ✱✱

6 —— It has been raining

Washington

Light snow falling

Weather Service Station

Preparing a weather map.

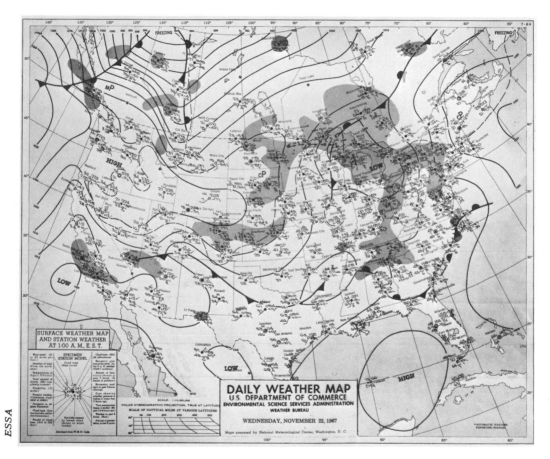

SURFACE WEATHER MAP
AND STATION WEATHER
AT 1:00 A.M., E.S.T.

SPECIMEN
STATION MODEL

DAILY WEATHER MAP
U.S. DEPARTMENT OF COMMERCE
ENVIRONMENTAL SCIENCE SERVICES ADMINISTRATION
WEATHER BUREAU

WEDNESDAY, NOVEMBER 22, 1967

Maps prepared by National Meteorological Center, Washington, D. C.

A weather map prepared at NMC.

*The station report as
it appears on a weather map.*

Meteorologists do their own analysis and prepare a weather map.

The four forecast maps—for twelve, twenty-four, thirty-six, and forty-eight hours—are then sent out to the local weather stations. The maps go out on electronic machines that actually send pictures over wires. These machines are called facsimiles.

The facsimile works somewhat like the teletype. The weather map, with its curved lines and numbers, is placed in the sending facsimile machine. An electric eye scans back and forth. The exact

The automatic data plotter
draws the lines showing
the computer analysis.

picture it "sees" appears immediately on facsimiles at all the Weather Service stations that are connected into the same circuit.

The local Weather Service receives more than forecasts from the facsimiles. Satellite photos, maps that show the weather conditions at various upper-air levels, and long-range forecasts are also received on the twelve facsimile circuits from the NMC.

The map is placed in the sending facsimile machine. It will immediately appear on the facsimiles at the local Weather Service stations.

Weather maps and satellite photos being received on the facsimile.

Every Weather Service station in the nation receives a wealth of weather information via teletypes and facsimiles. The meterologists at the station benefit from the valuable services of the NMC. The local forecaster keeps the summaries and forecasts prepared by the NMC close at hand as he starts to build the all-important weather forecast for his own area.

THE FORECASTER

The forecaster arrives at his forecast in an unusual way. He spends a few minutes studying the forecasts from the NMC or from a regional forecast center. He glances at the chart of the morning upper-air balloon launch. He thumbs through the surface reports from the last few days. He discusses the weather summaries with another meteorologist. Back and forth he goes, from report to summary to map to forecast.

This is the way the forecaster digests the mass of information that is available to him. In his mind he is putting these facts in order. All the while, he thinks about what he will say in his local weather forecast.

As he studies the maps from the NMC he looks for air masses. An air mass is a large body of air that has the same temperature and humidity and moves as a unit. As the air masses collide, and move over or under each other, they create different kinds of weather. He pays special attention to the front of each air mass. Most stormy weather occurs here.

The upper-air charts tell him more about the air masses. He looks for the height of the air mass near the station. A deep air mass moves more slowly than a shallow one. The speed of the wind at different heights also gives him a clue to the speed of movement of the air mass.

The forecaster is very interested in the air pressure measurements from the surface report. Falling pressure usually means that bad weather is on its way. Rising pressure usually means that the air will be clear and dry. The forecaster examines the other entries in the Daily Record for any information that they might give about changes in the weather.

Then the forecaster looks back at previous reports. He traces the changes and movements in the weather over the last few days. This review of past weather makes it easier to predict weather changes.

Despite the mass of data and information that is available from his own station, and despite all the help that he receives from NMC, it is still very difficult for one man, working alone, to produce an accurate weather forecast. For that reason, the forecaster often discusses the weather picture with other meteorologists at the station. Two scientists can sometimes reach a better understanding of the weather than just one.

Finally, though, the forecaster applies his own training and

The forecaster studies the charts, maps, and reports as he prepares his weather forecast.

experience to the problem of predicting the weather. He recalls similar weather conditions that have occurred in the past and the weather that resulted. He thinks of the features of the countryside near the station, such as mountains, big cities, rivers, or lakes, that influence the local weather. He uses the feeling and instinct for the weather that he has developed over the years.

After perhaps an hour of such preparations, the forecaster is ready to write out his forecast. Now he must put his thoughts into words.

As he writes, he carefully weighs each word. Should he call it "breezy" or "windy"? Is it to be "cold or "cool"? "Generally" or "mostly"? Is it to be 40 percent or 50 percent chance of rain? Many words are crossed out and changed as he searches for the best words to describe the weather. The forecast must be as clear and accurate as possible.

It takes him about fifteen minutes to write out the forecast. He checks it through again and again. Each time he finds a word or two to change. Finally he is satisfied.

He hurries into the communication room with his forecast. The handwritten copy goes on a rack alongside the teletype. He sits down and types out his forecast. Within seconds all the connected teletypes automatically type out the exact same forecast.

The forecaster sends his forecast out on the teletype.

Four regular forecasts are prepared every day—usually at five and eleven in the morning, five in the afternoon, and ten in the evening. The times are chosen to spread the forecasts out over the day, and to have them available for the early morning hours, for the noon, 6 P.M, and 11 P.M. television and radio news programs.

There are also other special forecasts to be made. There are regional forecasts. There are forecasts designed only for ships, for planes, or for farmers. There are forecasts on forest fires and flood dangers. There are long-range forecasts.

Making reliable forecasts is one of the most basic and important activities of the Weather Service. And the Weather Service has become very skilled and successful in its forecasting. Nearly nine out of every ten forecasts issued today turn out to be correct.

AIR POLLUTION FORECASTER

One of the newest members of the Weather Service team is the air pollution forecaster. Pollution observations did not become a part of the Weather Service program until 1955. Today air pollution is one of the major concerns of the Weather Service— just as it is one of the main worries of the general public.

People first became aware that pollution was a serious problem on October 26, 1948. There seemed to be nothing special about that day in the bleak factory town of Donora, Pennsylvania. A heavy fog blanketed the area. But that often happened on fall days. The tall smokestacks of the large steel mills and other factories and the chimneys of the coal-heated houses all belched clouds of smoke into the air. That happened every day.

But as this day went on, people in Donora realized that the fog and smoke were getting thicker and darker. Soon every person, every building, everything was covered with filthy black grime.

By midafternoon it was so dark that people were getting lost in their own neighborhoods. Drivers had to get out of their cars to read the street signs.

The doctors' offices were filled with patients—coughing, vomiting, and gasping for breath. About 6,000 of Donora's 14,000 people became seriously sick. Of these, at least twenty people died —victims of this first pollution tragedy.

In the years since 1948, pollution has grown much worse. The record number of deaths caused by pollution came in 1952, when 4,000 people in London, England, were killed in just a few days.

In recent years we have made some progress in preventing the air pollution that caused the mass killings. But, at the same time, pollution has spread. There are few areas left on earth with completely clean air. Gases and particles that cause pollution are blown to every corner of the world by the wind.

The Weather Service's pollution expert cooperates with other government agencies. He is mainly responsible for the meteorology of pollution. Others measure the amount and types of pollutants in the air. They find the man-made sources of the pollutants. And they enforce the anti-pollution laws.

The air pollution forecaster in the Weather Service depends largely on data collected by the upper-air balloons. He is especially interested in the temperature and wind measurements at various heights above the ground.

A scientist at a city agency tests how air pollution affects different metals and paints. The tall pipe brings air down to a lab for analysis.

The glass pipe near the ceiling carries air from the roof to the different testing machines at a city air-pollution lab.

He uses these figures in a series of mathematical equations. The result is a number which gives the ability of the air to remove the pollution.

This figure is combined with actual measurements of the gases and smokes that are in the air. A report is then issued, describing the pollution level as either good, acceptable, unsatisfactory, or unhealthy. A forecast is also made of the expected quality of the air for the following day.

These reports and forecasts are carefully watched by city officials. Whenever the pollution rises to the unsatisfactory level, they take steps to reduce the amount of pollution. Their actions range from postponing the burning of the city's garbage, all the way to forbidding cars to enter the city during a time of great danger.

The air pollution forecaster knows that the worst pollution emergencies, such as those in Donora and London, are caused by one particular weather pattern. It occurs when a level of warm air is sitting above a level of cool air at the surface. This is called a temperature inversion.

Normally, warm air at the surface rises into the cold air above. As it rises, it carries the pollutants away.

During a temperature inversion, though, the warm level of air acts as a lid. It does not allow the surface air to rise. The surface air is stuck—it cannot move.

Meanwhile the factories, furnaces, and automobiles continue to pour their gases and smokes into the air. These poisons just sit there, making the air dirtier and darker and more dangerous. Only when the inversion is broken, and the air begins to circulate, is the pollution cleared away.

A temperature inversion traps the pollution from this factory, not letting it spread out in the atmosphere.

The weather scientist cannot prevent pollution. Only a public determined to improve the quality of the air can do that. But he can warn of a temperature inversion or other dangerous conditions. This has already saved many lives. The pollution meteorol-

ogist can also learn more about the relationship between the weather and pollution. Increased understanding will reduce the terrible loss of life, the sickness, and the destruction of property now caused by pollution.

THE CLIMATOLOGIST

One of the meteorologists at the Weather Service station is not too interested in daily weather changes. He is more concerned with long-range weather patterns. Weather conditions over a long period of time make up the climate. The scientist who is an expert in this branch of meteorology is the climatologist.

The climatologist is skilled in both meteorology and in mathematics. He is the record keeper of the Weather Service. He collects, organizes, and stores the daily records of weather observations. He keeps charts that show the long-range weather changes. He prepares lists that show the highest, lowest, and average figures on various aspects of the weather.

Do you want to know the weather on the day you were born? Do you want to know whether summers are growing warmer? Do you want to know the wind speed on the day that tiles were blown off your roof? Do you want to know the type of weather to expect when you move to a new city?

All these questions can be answered by the climatologist.

Modern climatology really began during World War II, in the 1940s. The climatologist was able to offer valuable guidance to the military planners. The commanders had to know what weather to expect before sending men, planes, and ships into battle. The climatologist was able to describe the usual weather patterns in many of the lands in which Americans were fighting. The weather forecaster then filled in the weather details as the time of the operations approached.

Since then, the uses of climatology have greatly increased. The farmer uses climate information to decide which crops to grow. The engineer needs to know wind conditions before he lays out a new airport runway. The architect gets average temperature readings to decide what size air-conditioners to install. The highway department asks about the heaviest snowfall expected, to determine what size snowplows to buy.

The main office of the Weather Service's climatology service is the National Weather Records Center in Asheville, North Carolina. On its ten miles of shelves is stored an astounding amount of weather information. There are diaries and journals of men that kept weather records in the eighteenth century. For instance, did you know that on July 4, 1776, in Philadelphia, the date and place of the signing of the Declaration of Independence, the average temperature was 72 degrees?

The climatologist consults a record book to answer a question.

Today observations pour into the National Weather Records Center at the rate of over 100 million weather observations a year. Just as the forecaster bases his forecasts on material from the NMC, so the climatologist bases his records on material from the National Weather Records Center.

Besides acting as the record keeper for the Weather Service, the climatologist also does research and investigates special problems in climatology. He is always seeking new ways to help those seeking climatological information.

THE HURRICANE HUNTERS

A Weather Service plane taxied slowly out to the runway. Powerful winds sent sheets of rain pounding against the plane. No other planes were taking off or landing. In fact, no other planes were anywhere to be seen.

This was not just a bad storm. This was a hurricane—the most violent and destructive storm known to man. Planes do not usually fly during a hurricane.

But at the controls of this plane was one of the crack pilots of the Hurricane Hunter Squadron. Inside the plane were several scientists from the Weather Service, along with a full load of advanced meteorological equipment. Their mission was to fly

ESSA

One of the Hurricane Hunters heading into a bad storm.

right into the storm and report on conditions inside the hurricane to the meteorologists on the ground.

This is perhaps the most dangerous flight a pilot can make. The winds inside a hurricane can blow at speeds as high as 200 miles an hour. But these are remarkably skillful pilots. Although they recognize the danger, they do not hesitate to head right into the worst storms. They fly these dangerous missions to learn more about hurricanes and to keep a close watch on their progress.

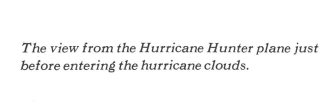

The view from the Hurricane Hunter plane just before entering the hurricane clouds.

ESSA

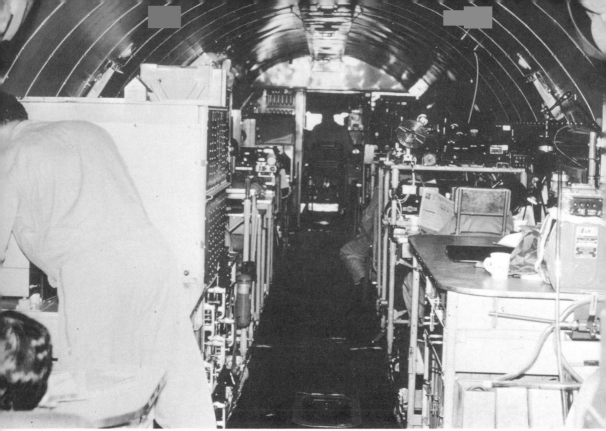

The men and equipment inside the Hurricane Hunter plane.

The Hurricane Hunter Squadron is connected with the National Hurricane Center, at Miami, Florida. All of the observing and forecasting of hurricanes, at Weather Service stations and in the air, is coordinated by the National Hurricane Center.

This hurricane was first noticed by a hurricane expert at a ground station. He was studying a cloud picture taken by a weather satellite. In the midst of a smooth cloud cover he saw a disturbance, a roughness in the clouds. He immediately became alert. A hurricane might be developing out at sea.

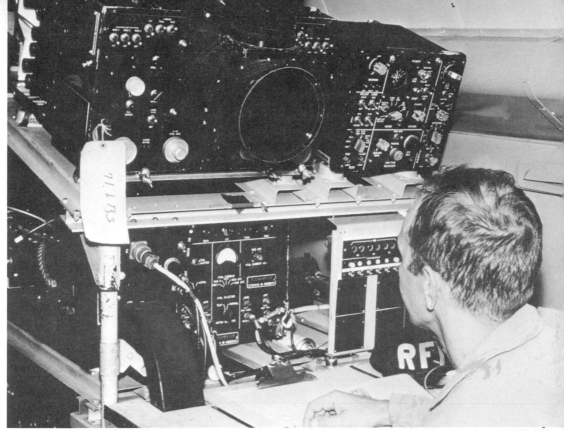

This meteorologist is watching the hurricane on the radar screen inside the plane.

The scientist anxiously awaited the next satellite photo coming in on the facsimile. His worst fears were justified. The clouds looked like they had been whipped into a giant swirl, covering hundreds of miles. They had taken on the famous hurricane shape.

The hurricane expert sent out a teletype message to the radar stations along the Gulf of Mexico. He warned them that a hurricane might be forming. At each of these stations, the radar operators watched their screens for signs of the hurricane.

Reports came in from automatic weather stations bobbing in

the Gulf. Their figures showed a sudden drop in air pressure at the same time as strong, gusty winds were starting.

By the next day it was certain that a good-sized hurricane had formed. And it was definitely moving toward the Texas coast. The Weather Service alerted the public to the danger of the approaching storm.

It issued an announcement, called an advisory. The advisory assigned a name to the hurricane. The name is taken from one of four lists of girls' names that are used each year. This hurricane was named Juno. (Actually, Juno is an imaginary hurricane. It is a combination of Alma and Inez, two real hurricanes of the 1966 season.)

The weathermen followed Juno carefully. They looked at photos from the weather satellites and the radar screens. They read reports from Weather Service stations and from the ships and automatic weather stations in the area. In addition, the Hurricane Hunter Squadron followed the storm.

Winds near the center of Juno were blowing at speeds of about 70 miles an hour. Gusts of wind reached over 100 miles an hour. Juno was slowly heading toward the Texas coast.

By the third day the weatherman issued a forecast of where and when Juno would strike. He put part of the Texas coast on a hurricane watch. This was a first warning for the most dangerous areas.

On the fourth day the winds near the center of Juno were well over 100 miles an hour. But the storm suddenly changed its course. It turned east and was heading for the Florida coast. The weatherman issued a hurricane warning. This meant that he expected Juno to strike land within twenty-four hours.

ESSA

The giant swirl of hurricane clouds as seen from a satellite.

Radio and television and the newspapers carried the news to the people. Families living near the low coastal areas were moved to safe high ground, since flooding is one of the biggest hurricane dangers. People were urged to lay in a supply of food that did not need refrigeration. They were told how to protect their homes, cars, and boats. Emergency crews of police and firemen were put on the alert. Telephone, gas, and electric companies got ready for

The hurricane forecasters study satellite photos and weather maps as they track and trace the hurricane.

the storm. Doctors and hospitals prepared to care for the injured.

The next day Juno hit. It smashed into the coast of Florida, just as the weatherman had forecast. Winds of nearly 150 miles an hour raged near the center of the storm. Tides were many feet above normal. Huge waves crashed over the seawalls. About ten inches of rain came pouring down, adding to the coastal flooding.

As the hurricane slowly moved north, it lost some of its energy.

ESSA

The hurricane strikes. Powerful winds and raging seas batter the coast.

The winds began to calm down and there was less rain. The following day Juno headed east, out over the Atlantic Ocean. After a day or two it quietly disappeared.

Juno was an average hurricane. Yet, it left behind miles and miles of destruction. It cost about $20 million to repair the damage done by this one storm.

Because the Weather Service gave early and accurate warnings of the hurricane, no lives were lost. Everyone was able to take shelter. Scientists are working toward the day when they will be able to tame the hurricanes, and lessen their terrible destruction.

THE TORNADO FORECASTER

The strongest winds on earth are found in the swirling centers of tornadoes. In fact, the speeds are so great that no instrument has yet been built that can measure these winds.

A tornado is a small storm. Its path is seldom more than sixteen miles long and one-quarter of a mile wide. It usually lasts only a short time. Yet, a tornado can cause a vast amount of havoc and damage.

In just a few minutes a tornado can turn a street lined with trees and solid buildings into a pile of scrap wood and rubble. It can pick up houses, trains, and cars and dash them down many

As the tornado speeds along, it picks up dust and dirt, turning the funnel dark and black.

yards away. It can lift people and animals and fling them great distances.

Tornadoes strike anywhere, anytime. Mostly, though, they hit the Midwestern states during the spring months. About one out of every four tornadoes comes between four and six in the late afternoon.

The Weather Service has organized a team of meteorologists who are experts in recognizing and forecasting tornadoes. Most of them are stationed in the Midwest, in the tornado belt. The center of the Weather Service's tornado service is at the National Severe Storm Forecast Center in Kansas City, Missouri.

The familiar funnel shape of an approaching tornado.

Day and night, all year round, Weather Service tornado forecasters are on duty. They watch for the first hint of a tornado. They have the ability to spot a storm that will develop into a tornado, and then accurately forecast the path it will follow.

Perhaps the most dramatic proof of their skill came on April 11, 1965, the date of some of the worst tornadoes in history.

The tornado forecaster on duty that morning was making a routine analysis of the 9 A.M. surface weather map. Something caught his eye. A mass of cold air from Canada was heading south over the midwestern states. At the same time, a mass of warm air from the Gulf of Mexico was moving north toward the same part of the country. They were heading straight at each other.

*A rare set of pictures
from 1944 showing
the development of a tornado.*

He took a close look at the upper-air charts. The measurements of pressure, winds, and temperature convinced him that there would be serious tornadoes before the day was over.

The forecaster checked and rechecked his figures. He wanted to be sure and as exact as possible when he made his forecast. The people in the path of the tornado had to be warned. Yet he did not want to give a false alarm to the people in safe areas.

Finally, at 10:45 A.M., he was ready. He issued a tornado watch, saying, "Several tornadoes are expected this afternoon from 1 to 7 P.M., across parts of Missouri, Illinois, and Indiana." The watch was broadcast to the public over radio and television.

Suddenly he detected a change in the weather. The storm

99

center turned and started heading toward the northeast. The forecaster used a high-speed computer to help him predict the storm's movement. The computer agreed with his forecast that the storm was taking a new direction. The revised one o'clock tornado watch said that the tornadoes would probably move across areas of Wisconsin, Iowa, and Illinois.

It is easy to trace the tornado's path as it tore through this city.

ESSA

By two o'clock the storm picked up both strength and speed. It was moving forward at about 50 miles an hour. The forecaster began sending out tornado warnings, pinpointing the areas of greatest danger.

Then—the tornadoes struck. Thirty-seven separate tornadoes roared through cities and towns, fields and forests. Houses were smashed as though they were made of paper. Cars and trains were tossed around like children's toys. Giant trees were uprooted. Anything and everything in the paths of the tornadoes was ripped to pieces.

Some people had heeded the Weather Service warnings. They had taken shelter in storm cellars and were safe from the tornado's fury overhead. Others, though, did not hear the warnings or chose to ignore them. April 11, 1965, was Palm Sunday, and many families were at church or visiting. Nearly three hundred people were killed and about five thousand injured. The damage to property was estimated at $300 million.

Of the thirty-seven tornadoes on that fateful day, all but four struck within the area and time forecast by the Weather Service. No one can guess how many lives were saved by the skillful work of the tornado forecasters.

THE FLOOD FORECASTER

During December, 1968, record amounts of snow fell on the states of Minnesota and North and South Dakota. Temperatures for the month were below average. The snow stayed on the ground.

Some weathermen in the area began to think ahead to the spring. They realized that the snow would begin to melt during the spring rain season. Many of the meteorologists concluded that there was a danger of very serious floods.

Hydrologists, weather scientists who are experts in floods, began to study the problem. They measured the amount of snow on the ground and calculated how much water there would be when it melted. They studied the water level in the rivers and the moisture in the soil. From the climatologist they learned how much rain normally fell during the spring.

On February 11, the public was warned to begin preparations for major spring floods. The Weather Service started sending out weekly reports on the developing flood situation.

President Richard Nixon ordered the Army Corps of Engineers, the Departments of Agriculture and Transportation, and other federal agencies to cooperate with the Weather Service in preparing for the floods. State and local governments joined in the effort. The entire action was given the name Operation Foresight.

The first goal of Operation Foresight was to collect more information on the flood danger. The Army and Air Force provided weather observations from their planes and radar posts. Satellite photos were measured to determine the extent of the snow covering the ground. All of the Weather Service stations in the area made frequent measurements of snow depth, rate of melting, and amount of moisture in the ground. Hydrologists were flown to remote spots to measure snow depth. Even gravediggers were asked to report on the frost level in the earth.

During the first week in March there were several days of heavy rainfall. The soil was soaked. Everyone agreed that it could not hold any more water. To make matters worse, the temperature rose, and the snow started to melt. The danger of record floods was growing ever stronger.

Operation Foresight directed the building of levees, dikes, and sandbag walls to protect homes and other buildings. Any property or machinery that could be moved was taken to high ground. Emergency communication systems were set up.

ESSA

Dikes helped to protect some homes during the 1969 floods.

Farmers were helped to harvest crops, even though they were not quite ripe. Grain that was in storage was shipped to cities in other parts of the country. Farm animals were removed to safety.

Most of all, preparations were made to care for the people in the areas that would be hit by floods. Food, clothing, and shelter were made ready for those who would be driven from their homes.

On March 13, the Weather Service put out a detailed flood report. It forecast the highest levels that the rivers would reach at over two hundred points in the ten Midwestern states.

For the next thirty days, nearly four thousand miles of river flooded over their banks. Farms, roads, whole cities were under

The floodwaters almost completely cover these houses.
The people on the roof of the front, center house are awaiting rescue.

ESSA

water. Ten people lost their lives, twenty-five thousand were forced to flee their homes, and property worth $100 million was destroyed. It was the worst flood ever to hit this part of the country.

No one knows how much more death and destruction there would have been without Operation Foresight and the Weather Service warnings. The forecasts were very accurate. More than one-third of the forecasts made on March 13 were correct to within one foot of the actual crest of the water. Later forecasts were correct to within a few inches. Considering that some rivers rose as much as thirty-five feet, this was a remarkable achievement.

Every year nearly one million Americans are driven from their homes by floods. The damage is estimated at over one billion dollars. The hydrologists in the Weather Service are the front line of defense against these natural disasters. They watch for the approaching danger of floods and warn the public where and when the flooding will occur.

Hydrologists are also leaders in research into the relation between water and the weather. They want to know more about the causes of too much water (floods), too little water (drought), and dirty water (pollution). Their goal is to help all men have the right amount of clean water for their needs.

SPACEFLIGHT METEOROLOGISTS

Weather scientists are the unsung heroes of space shots. The successful test, launch, and return of every rocket depends on Weather Service experts in spaceflight meteorology.

The spaceflight meteorologists instruct engineers on the best time to test the rockets. People in nearby communities are less annoyed by the roar of the noisy engines under the right set of weather conditions.

The launch, too, depends on favorable weather conditions. Strong winds before launch can easily topple the tall rocket. A bolt of lightning might damage or destroy the rocket on the

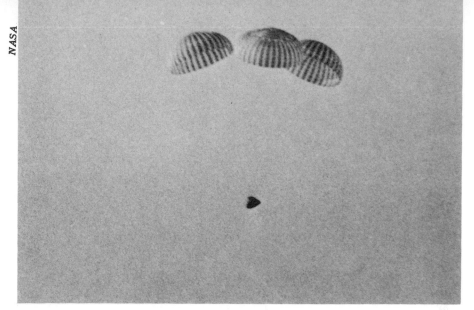

Apollo 13 parachuting in for a perfect splash-down, after being given a forecast of good weather by Spaceflight Meteorology.

launch pad. Fog, low clouds, or poor visibility at launch time cause other difficulties.

The most crucial test for weather forecasters, however, comes at splashdown. Bad weather can ruin the parachute descent, swamp the spaceship, and interfere with the search during recovery. Gemini 5 was brought down one orbit early to avoid Hurricane Betsy. Apollo 11, scheduled to land in an area where the Weather Service forecast rain and possible thunderstorms, splashed down at a point two hundred miles away. The spaceship landed in perfect weather.

During April, 1970, the entire world listened for the forecast of the Spaceflight Meteorology group that was guiding the moon-shot, Apollo 13. There had been an explosion in the service module. Now the crippled ship containing the three astronauts was returning to earth ahead of schedule, without having landed on the moon.

Apollo 13 blasts off for the trip to the moon.
Spaceflight meteorologists carefully watched
the weather to choose the best day for the launch.
NASA

109

The spaceflight group studied the forecast of the NMC for weather conditions in the chosen site. But the usual northern hemisphere forecast prepared by the NMC was not enough. The weather at the landing site was being influenced by a giant weather system that extended into both the northern and southern hemispheres. The spaceflight meteorologist needed a weather forecast for the entire globe.

For some time the scientists at the NMC had been working on the creation of a computer program that would analyze and forecast the weather for the entire world. In spite of the fact that it had never been used before, scientists decided to use this program to predict the weather for the landing site chosen for Apollo 13.

They fed all the data they had collected into the computer. The computer produced a thirty-six hour forecast of wind flow and air pressure. This was given to the experts in the spaceflight group to serve as the basis for their forecast. In addition, the scientists brought together data on surface and air observations, reports from airplanes that were crisscrossing the area, cloud pictures, and temperature measurements from four weather satellites.

At first, the outlook was bad. A tropical storm, Helen, was heading for the EOM (End of Mission) point. Rescue would be difficult, or impossible, if the astronauts landed in the middle of a storm.

Ground control for Apollo 13 explored other landing plans. But the spaceship had little power left, and there was not much that they could do to change the End of Mission site.

Meanwhile Apollo 13 was hurtling toward earth. For a while it looked as though the capsule and Helen were heading toward the same place in the Pacific and would arrive at the same time.

Then, the weathermen noticed that Helen had veered off to

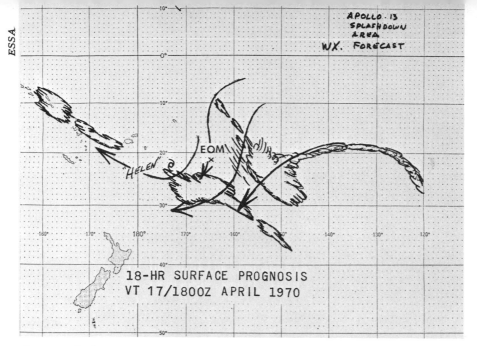

18-HR SURFACE PROGNOSIS
VT 17/1800Z APRIL 1970

A part of the actual weather map used to choose the End of Mission site for the crippled Apollo 13 spaceship.

the side. Was it changing its path? Would it go back again to its old direction? There was little time to think or discuss the matter. The lives of the astronauts hung in the balance. From the data that they had, they decided that Helen was moving away. They sent a message: ALL CLEAR.

The rest of the Apollo 13 mission is part of history. Apollo 13 came down in perfect weather, in one of the best on-target landings of any space flight.

The spaceflight meteorologists keep busy, even between missions. They examine the weather information that they supplied for the last flight to see if they provided the best possible service. They seek ways to improve their reporting and forecasting. And they research new projects, such as the use of laser beams to communicate with spaceships, to extend their ability in space-flight meteorology.

CHANGING THE WEATHER

The scientists at the Weather Service do not believe the saying "Everyone talks about the weather, but no one does anything about it."

Many weathermen perform experiments on ways to change and improve the weather. They are learning how to make rain or snow, get rid of fog, weaken lightning, as well as lessen the fury of hurricanes.

The idea of man changing the weather is not a new one. Ancient tribes built giant fires in the hope of creating rain clouds. In some lands, primitive people threw rocks or shot arrows at advancing storms to ward off damaging hailstones. Over the centuries church

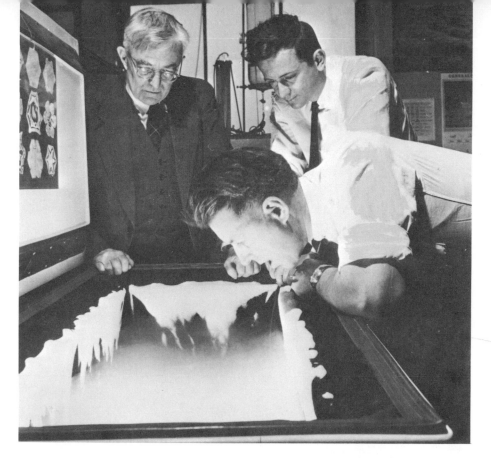

Vincent J. Schaefer found that his breath turned into ice crystals when he breathed into a home freezer that was super-cooled with dry ice. Watching him are Irving Langmuir and Bernard Vonnegut, his co-workers in the General Electric Research Laboratory.

bells and cannon shots have been used to bring rain to drought areas.

The scientific period of weather change, or modification, however, began in 1946. Vincent J. Schaefer found, by accident, that when he breathed into a super-cooled freezer, tiny ice crystals formed. From this observation grew the idea of trying to form ice raindrops in the air.

These clouds were chosen for a silver iodide seeding experiment by the Weather Service.

The same clouds nine minutes after seeding with silver iodide.

Nineteen minutes later the clouds have taken on this shape.

A half hour after seeding. Rain has already begun to fall.

Since then there have been several successful experiments in rainmaking. The basic method has been cloud seeding—dropping particles of dry ice or silver iodide crystals into a cloud. Dry ice super-cools the cloud, causing an ice crystal to form around each dry ice particle.

Silver iodide crystals are very similar in shape to crystals of ice. When silver iodide is released in a cloud, ice forms around each crystal. Then, as they fall they melt, and it rains.

Scientists have different opinions of seeding. Some say that it is too difficult to tell whether rain that falls during an experiment is caused by seeding or whether it would have rained anyway. Almost no one believes that rain can be made to fall where there is no chance of rain. More or less, they agree with the government report which says that local rainfall can be increased about 10 percent by seeding.

Weather modification is also being used in an effort to cut the damage and destruction caused by hurricanes. Project Stormfury was begun in 1962 to learn more about hurricanes and to search for ways to modify these storms.

In the summer of 1969, Hurricane Debbie was chosen for a major Operation Stormfury experiment. The winds near the center of the hurricane on August 18 were whipping about at speeds as high as 113 miles an hour. The hurricane clouds were seeded. Several hours later, the highest winds were only 78 miles an hour.

The following day there was no seeding. The storm winds grew very strong once again. On August 20, therefore, it was decided that Hurricane Debbie was to be seeded again. Later that day the strongest winds had dropped from 114 miles an hour to 97 miles an hour.

Hurricane Debbie was closely watched during Operation Stormfury. This satellite picture was taken on August 18, 1969.

A satellite photo of Debbie taken on August 19.

ESSA

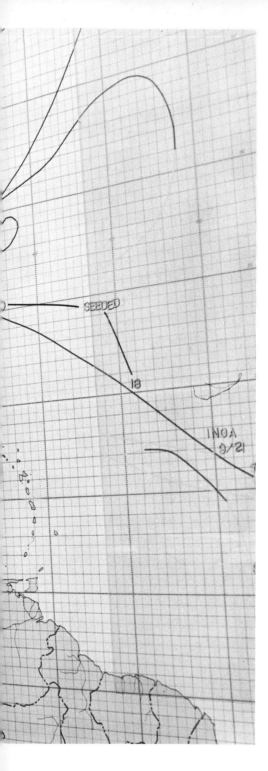

SEEDED

18

INOA
9/21

All hurricanes,
including Debbie, are tracked
at the National Hurricane Center.
(Debbie's path is to the right
of the photo.)

These results are not absolute proof that seeding weakened the hurricane. But the scientists of Project Stormfury believe that they are on the road to success. They point out that if the damage from just one hurricane is reduced by as little as one percent, it will save more money than the total spent on Project Stormfury.

Other studies have tested methods of eliminating dangerous lightning bolts from striking the earth. One promising approach is to scatter tiny lengths of metal threads in the clouds. The threads may be able to short-circuit the lightning, not allowing dangerous bolts to build up.

Fog is another hazard that meteorologists would like to be able to "do something about." Presently, cold-weather fog can be treated with seeding. Warm-weather fog, though, cannot be dispersed in this way. As yet, no practical method of removing warm fog has been found.

Everyone agrees that hurricanes should be weakened, and that there should be rain in drought-stricken areas. But should clouds be seeded if the farmer needs rain, but the amusement park owner wants no rain? What if seeding causes it to snow on one side of the mountain, and no snow falls on the ski resorts on the other side? There are important legal questions to be answered before there can be widespread use of weather modification.

The future of weather modification is also closely tied to the growth of the entire science of meteorology. With more accurate forecasting over long periods of time, computer models of the weather, use of satellites, better seeding, and other methods, the weatherman may yet do something about the weather, to the benefit of all mankind.

FURTHER READING

ADLER, IRVING, *Weather in Your Life*. New York, John Day, 1959.
BIXBY, WILLIAM, *Skywatchers*. New York, McKay, 1962.
NAVARRA, JOHN GABRIEL, *Wide World Weather*. New York, Doubleday, 1968.
WOLFE, LOUIS, *The Wonders of the Atmosphere*. New York, Putnam, 1962.
    General books on the weather.

JAKES, JOHN, *TIROS, Weather Eye in Space*. New York, Messner, 1966.
STAMBLER, IRWIN, *Weather Instruments*. New York, Putnam, 1968.
    The tools of the weathermen.

SCHNEIDER, HERMAN, *Everyday Weather and How It Works*. New York, McGraw-Hill, 1961.

SPILHAUS, ATHELSTAN F., *Weathercraft*. New York, Viking, 1951.
How to make your own weather instruments and forecasts.

INDEX

Air mass, 71
Air pollution forecaster, 75-81
Anemometer, 29
Apollo 13, 109-111

Barometer, 30, 32, 33, 36

Ceiling balloon, 20
Ceilometer, 21
Climatologist, 82-83, 103
Cloud seeding, 116, 120
Communication room, 51, 56

Computer, 61, 63, 100, 110

Daily Record, 19, 26, 30, 33, 45
Donora, Pennsylvania, 75-76, 79
Dry ice, 116

Facsimiles, 67-69, 89
Flood forecaster, 102-106

Hurricane, 60
   advisory, 90
   forecasters, 85-94
   warning, 90

Hurricane Hunter Squadron, 85-88, 90
Hydrologist, 102, 103, 106
Hygrometer, 30, 36
Hygrothermometer, 30

London, England, 76, 79

National Hurricane Center, 88
National Meteorological Center (NMC), 54, 57, 59, 61, 62, 63, 68, 69, 70, 71, 84, 110
National Severe Storm Forecast Center, 97-100, 101
National Weather Records Center, 83, 84

Observational panel, 24, 26
Operation Foresight, 103, 106

Precipitation gage, 26
Project Stormfury, 116, 120

Radar operator, 46-51, 89
Radar screen, 46-49
Radiosonde, 36, 38, 39, 40, 44, 45

Schaefer, Vincent J., 113
Silver iodide crystals, 116
Spaceflight meteorologist, 106-111

Teletype, 52-53, 54, 56, 57, 61, 67, 69, 89
Temperature inversion, 79
Thermometer, 26, 36
TIROS, 59
Tornadoes, 95-101
    warning, 101
    watch, 99-100
Transmissometer, 23-24

Upper-air balloon (see Weather balloon)
Upper-air specialist, 35-45

Weather balloon, 35, 39, 40, 44, 45, 70, 76
Weather forecast, 54, 63, 67, 68, 69, 70-74, 79, 98, 99, 105, 106, 109, 110
Weather map, 54, 62, 63, 67, 68, 70, 71
Weather observer, 18-34
Weather report, 34, 51, 52, 62
Weather satellite, 59-61, 68, 103
    photo, 88, 89
Weather Service Stations, 14, 15, 18-19, 23, 34, 39, 46, 49-50, 51, 56
Weather vane, 26, 29

ABOUT THE AUTHOR

Melvin Berger was born in New York City. He was educated at City College; University of Rochester, where he received his Bachelor's Degree; Columbia University, where he earned his Master's Degree; and London University.

Mr. Berger loves to travel and it was during his travels that he made many side visits to laboratories. The idea for the series "Scientists at Work" grew + of these visits.

Mr. Berger lives with his wife and two daughters on Long Island, New York.